An ECS **Once Upon A Time**™ Book, Grades K-2

The Elves and the Shoemaker

Critical Thinking and Writing Activities
For the Emerging Reader

Arlene Capriola and Rigmor Swensen
Illustrated by Kathy Burns

Welcome to the Once Upon A Time™ series!

Learning to read should be fun! Children focus longer and retain more when they are doing activities they enjoy. The 10-book **Once Upon A Time**™ series teaches reading and writing as a fun, engaging process. Children create their own storybooks (complete with illustrations!) by elaborating on well-known fairy tales. Familiar story lines and colorful characters will amuse and entertain children for hours as they improve reading and writing skills.

The **Once Upon A Time**™ series is more than just fun. It is an effective means of advancing reading and writing levels. Educators agree that emerging readers should begin reading with materials that provide higher-level thinking skills and practice in following directions. Research emphasizes that reading and writing should begin simultaneously. The **Once Upon A Time**™ series provides these elements in a format attractive to children. Each book in the series encourages:

- Reading beyond the blank before answering, learning to use context clues
- Rereading each completed chapter, asking, "Does your story make sense?"
- Referring to the story for clues to answer TELL and GUESS questions
- Becoming involved in the story and risk-taking
- Reading directions carefully prior to drawing comprehension pictures
- Using complete sentences for all writing activities

Welcome to the fairy-tale world of learning with the **Once Upon A Time**™ series! Have fun!

About the Authors...

Arlene Capriola, an elementary reading specialist, holds a combined master's degree in reading and learning disabilities. She has three sons and resides with her husband, John, in Long Island, New York.

Rigmor Swensen is a freelance writer and former teacher of secondary reading and English literature. She holds a master's degree in reading and special education. Riggie, mother of three, lives in Long Island, New York, with her husband, Roy. She and Arlene have enjoyed collaborating on several reading workbook series.

 The Once Upon A Time™ series is also available on audio tapes!

To order, contact your local school supply store or –

ECS Learning Systems, Inc.
P.O. Box 791437
San Antonio, Texas 78279-1437

Editor: Cherisse Mastry
Cover/Page Layout & Graphics: Kirstin Simpson
Book Design: Educational Media Services

ISBN 1-57022-141-3

©1998 by ECS Learning Systems, Inc., San Antonio, Texas. All rights reserved. No part of this publication may be reproduced, stored in a retrieval system, or transmitted in any way or by any means (electronic, mechanical, photocopying, recording, or otherwise) without prior written permission from ECS Learning Systems, Inc., with the exceptions found below.

Photocopying of student worksheets by a teacher who purchased this publication for his/her own class is permissible. Reproduction of any part of this publication for an entire school or for a school system or for commercial sale is strictly prohibited. **Copyright infringement is a violation of Federal Law.**

Printed in the United States of America.

My Story about...

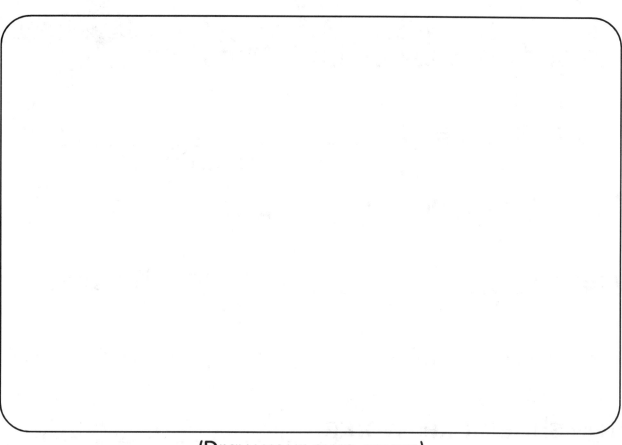

(Draw your own cover.)

The Elves and the Shoemaker

by

_____

(Write your name.)

Chapter 1

Long ago there was a shoemaker.

He and his wife had an old house.

It was at the end of _____ .
(town, down)

In the house he had a shop to sell shoes.

He _____ them on a big bench.
(ate, made)

He made the best _____ in town.
(shoes, feet)

The shoemaker worked _____ day.
(to, all)

At night he and his wife went up to bed.

The shoemaker did not make much money.

He and his wife were _____ poor.
(very, went)

Tell: Why was the shoemaker poor?

The shoemaker _____

_____

Here is the shoemaker's house.

- **Write** what he sells on the
- Make a picture and the word.

Chapter 2

One night the shoemaker was very sad.

He only had leather for one pair of shoes.

And he had _____ money to buy more.
(no, two)

He _____ at his bench.
(sat, rat)

"What will we do now?" he asked his wife.

"Do not be _____ sad," she said.
(at, so)

"Come _____ to bed.
(by, up)

By morning we may have some luck."

So he put the leather on the big bench.

Then he went to _____ .
(sea, bed)

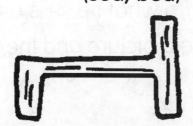

Guess: What will go on in the night?

In the night _____

_____

Here is the shoemaker's house.

- Put the things where they go:

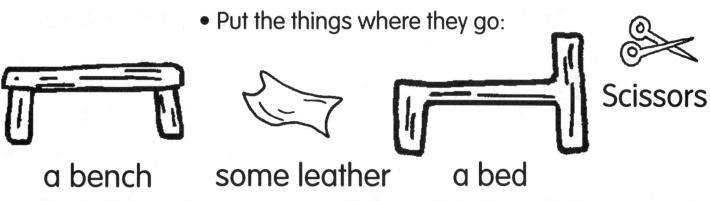

a bench   some leather   a bed   Scissors

Chapter 3

It _____ very late.
(was, did)

The shop was still.

Two elves danced in _____ door.
(it, the)

They were all in rags.

They hopped up on the big _____ .
(bench, hat)

And they went right to work.

As _____ worked, they sang a song.
(us, they)

"Tap, tap, tap, snap, snap, snap, one, two, three. We make shoes for all to see."

When the sun _____ up, they were done.
(been, came)

Then they danced out the door.

Tell: What did the elves do?

The elves _____

_____

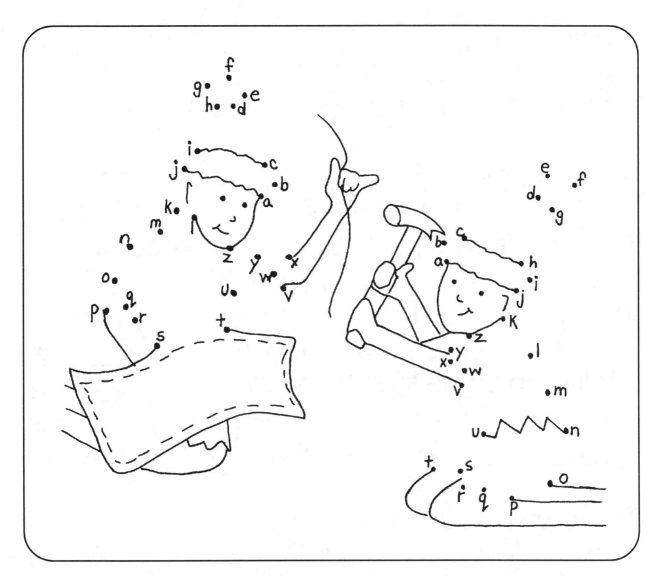

This is the shoemaker's shop.

• Go dot-to-dot to see who is here.

Chapter 4

The next day the shoemaker came down.

"Come here, quick!" he called to his wife.

"Do you see _____ I see?"
(what, why)

"I see a fine pair of shoes," said his wife.

"They are as _____ as the night."
(green, black)

"But who made them?" asked the shoemaker.

Just then, the bell _____ .
(rang, hid)

A tall man came into the shop.

"I _____ a pair of black shoes," he said.
(need, sit)

"Sit down," said the shoemaker.

"I have a surprise for you."

The tall _____ put on the shoes.
(fish, man)

Guess: Will the shoes fit the man?

_____ , the shoes _____
(Yes, No)

_____

The tall man is in the shop.

But 5 things are missing.
• Can you put them in?

Chapter 5

"They fit so _____ !
(hide, well)

I will pay a lot for the shoes," the man said.

Off he went in his _____ black shoes.
(new, dew)

The shoemaker was very happy.

That _____ he got more leather.
(pond, day)

He got leather for **two** pairs of shoes.

The shoemaker _____ home.
(fell, ran)

He put the leather on the big bench.

Then _____ went to bed.
(he, us)

Morning came.

The shoemaker went down to his shop.

Guess: What will the shoemaker see?

The shoemaker will see _____

_____

What will the tall man say about his shoes?

• Put the first letter for the pictures to see.

Chapter 6

The shoemaker had to rub his eyes.

"Do you see what I see?" he asked his wife.

"I see two pairs of ladies' shoes," she said.

"They are as red as _____!"
(snow, apples)

"But who made them?" asked the shoemaker.

Just then, the _____ bell rang.
(cat, door)

Two ladies came _____ .
(in, so)

"We want some red shoes," said the ladies.

"_____ down," said the shoemaker.
(Sit, Pat)

"I have a surprise for you."

The two ladies _____ on the shoes.
(put, sat)

Guess: Will the ladies like the shoes?

The ladies _____

_____

Who am I? Put the letter.

    A. We put on the red shoes.

    B. We make the shoes.

    C. I put out the leather.

    D. I got nice black shoes.

Chapter 7

"My, what pretty shoes!" said the ladies.

"We'll _____ them!"
　　　　(take, tell)

They gave the shoemaker a lot of money.

Off they went in the _____ red shoes.
　　　　　　　　　　　(new, and)

The shoemaker was very happy.

That day he got leather for **six** pairs of shoes.

He _____ it on his bench.
　　　(pop, put)

Then he _____ to bed.
　　　　(was, went)

Morning came.

The shoemaker went down to his shop.

There _____ were!
　　　(they, this)

Six pairs of yellow and blue and white shoes!

Guess: Will the shoemaker still be poor?

I think the shoemaker _____

_____

Here is the shoemaker with the new shoes.

- Make the shoes the colors in the story.
- **Color** the bench orange.
- Show how the shoemaker feels.

Chapter 8

And so it went.

Each night the shoemaker set out the leather.

Then he went to _____ .
(bed, bat)

And each morning he found more shoes.

Everyone in _____ came to his shop.
(book, town)

They wanted to buy his shoes.

Soon the shoemaker was very _____ .
(rich, big)

"We are very happy," said the shoemaker.

"But we do not know who makes the shoes."

"Let us stay up to _____ ," his wife said.
(see, sell)

So that night they did not go up to bed.

They _____ in back of the coats.
(hid, swam)

18 ©ECS Learning Systems, Inc., San Antonio, TX   All rights reserved

Guess: Will the elves come again?

_____ , the elves _____
(Yes, No)

_____

Who is in the shop? Color to see.

1 = orange   4 = yellow
2 = blue   5 = red
3 = green   6 = black

Chapter 9

It was very _____ .
(let, late)

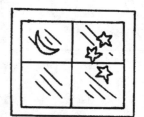

The shop was still.

The two little elves danced in the _____ .
(hat, door)

They were all in rags.

"Elves!" said the shoemaker.

"Shh!" said his _____ .
(dog, wife)

The elves hopped up on the big bench.

They _____ right to work.
(went, park)

As they worked, they _____ a song.
(sang, long)

"Tap, tap, tap, snap, snap, snap, one, two, three. We make shoes for all to see."

Guess: What will they do for the elves?

The shoemaker and his wife will _____

_____

The shoemaker and his wife hide by the coats.

What do they say?
- **Write** it.

Chapter 10

When morning came, the elves were gone.

The shoemaker and his wife came out.

They looked at the _____ shoes.
(fine, wide)

"These little elves have made us rich."

But they are all in rags!" the shoemaker _____ .
(said, see)

"I will make them _____ and coats.
(pots, hats)

I will make tops and pants," said his wife.

"You must make them _____ shoes."
(poor, little)

"Yes, yes!" said the shoemaker.

That night they put the gifts on the bench.

Then they hid in back of the _____ .
(coats, tail)

Guess: What will the elves do with the gifts?

The elves will _____

_____

The shoemaker put out gifts for the elves.

- Make them in the right spot.
- **Color** them your best colors.

Chapter 11

It was very late.

The _____ was still.
　　　(shop, map)

The two little elves danced in the door.

They hopped up on the big bench.

What a surprise _____ got!
　　　　　　　　(three, they)

The elves put _____ all the fine gifts.
　　　　　　(on, to)

Then they sang and danced with _____ .
　　　　　　　　　　　　　　　　(play, joy)

"Look, oh look, how fine are we.
No more cobblers will we be!"

They danced right out the _____ .
　　　　　　　　　　　　　(boat, door)

And they were never seen again.

The shoemaker was happy ever after.

The End

Guess: Where did the elves go?

I think the elves _____

_____

Make the pictures tell the story.

- Put 1 in the box that comes **first**.
- Put 2 in the box that comes **next**.
- Put 3 in the box that comes **last**.

Instant Recap

Make a rhyme about The Elves and the Shoemaker.
Write the words you need.
The first letter will help you.

The shoemaker made shoes all day.

But he had no money, sad to s __ __ .

Leather for just one pair he had.

So he went to bed so very s __ __ .

Two elves danced in, one by one.

Tap! Snap! The shoes were d __ __ __ .

The shoemaker had good shoes to sell,

To the man who rang the b __ __ __ .

Two ladies got the shoes so red.

Made when the shoemaker was in b __ __ .

Who made the shoes, no one did say.
But the shoemaker got rich day by d __ __ .

And so the shoemaker hid one night.
He looked and saw this funny s __ __ __ __ .

Two elves in rags worked all night long.
And as they worked they sang a s __ __ __ .

"Tap, tap, tap, snap, snap, snap,
one, two, three!
We make shoes for all to s __ __ ."

The shoemaker made them shoes to fit.
His wife made little pants, bit by b __ __ .

That night the elves put on the stuff.
And then they danced off in a p __ __ __ !

Here is a photo album.
Help tell the story of The Elves and the Shoemaker.

1. Here are the elves _____

2. Here are the elves _____

HAPPY BIRTHDAY TO THE ELVES

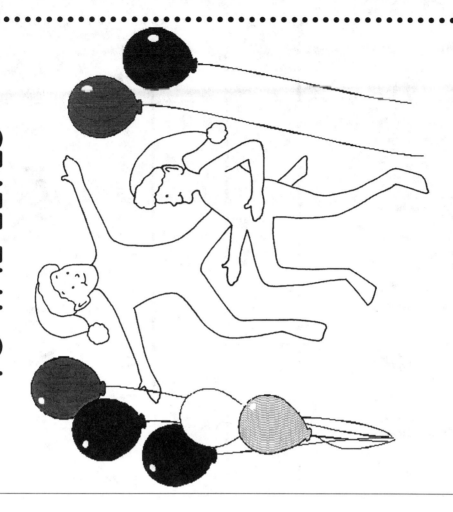

Here are the elves.

Put nice pants and tops on them.

Put pretty shoes on them, too.

It is the elves' birthday.
Let's send them a birthday card!

1. **Color** the card.
2. **Cut** along the dotted line.
3. **Fold** down the middle.

Dear Elves,
Happy birthday to you! I hope

_____
_____
_____

Your pal,
_____

The elves are 7 years old.

Draw the 🕯🕯🕯's on the cake.

Make the cake purple and yellow.

Author's Page

You are the author.
Draw your picture in the box below.

1. **Read** your story to five others.

2. **Tell** them to put their names below.

3. Let them **tell** you how they like your story.

4. Let them **tell** you how they like your pictures.

_____
(Write your name.)

_____   _____

_____   _____

_____   _____

NO LONGER THE PROPERTY
OF THE
UNIVERSITY OF R.I. LIBRARY